Find the Sentences

Put a circle around the sentences.

1. in the sand

(2. Nan went to see me)

3. It is a big hat

4. at 6:00

5. The cat had a nap

6. A red can

7. Sam has a dog

8. His dog can get the ball

9. on the box

How many did you find?

EMC 4023

Telling Sentences

A **period** is used at the end of a sentence that tells you something.

Put a . at the end of the sentences.

1. I am Jim

2. My sister is Ann

3. We can go to the park

4. It will be fun

5. We will see lions

6. We will see monkeys

7. Then we can eat ice cream

EMC 4023

Asking Sentences

A **question mark** is used at the end of a sentence that **asks** something.

Put a **?** at the end of the sentences.

1. Can you jump rope

2. Do you want to go to my house

3. Can we go to the pet shop

4. Was the dog funny

5. Is that a fox

6. What is that

7. Do you like pizza

EMC 4023

Start at 1.
Connect the dots.

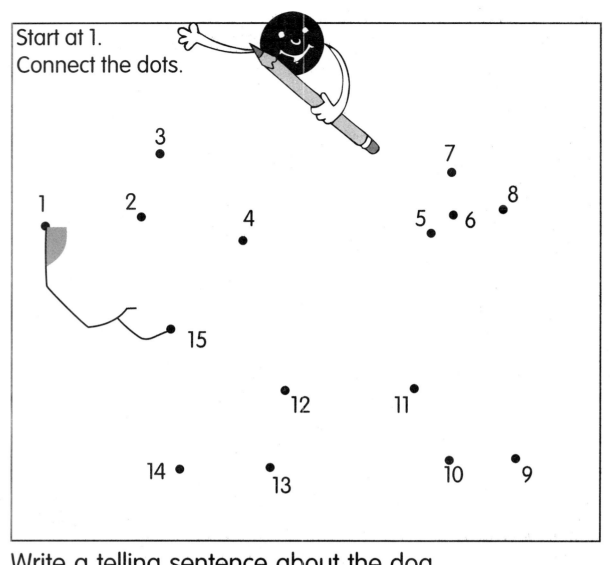

Write a telling sentence about the dog.

_____

- -

_____

- -

Write an asking sentence about the dog.

_____

- -

_____

- -

4

Capital Letters

Trace.

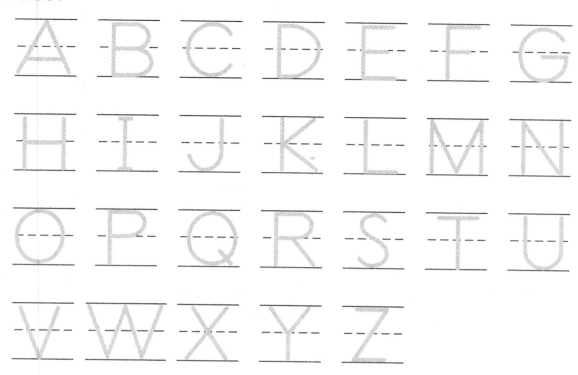

Write.

EMC 4023

Names start with capital letters.

A H T
B N C
D K E Q Y

A B C D E F G H I J K L M N O P Q R S T U V W X Y Z

ann   _Ann_   bob

kim   dan

jamal   ben

jose   nancy

My name is _____

EMC 4023

The days of the week start with capital letters.

monday   Monday

tuesday

wednesday

thursday

friday

saturday

sunday

Today is

EMC 4023

A sentence starts with a capital letter.

Fill in the capital letters.

1. M̲y pet is not big.

2. it cannot run and hop.

3. my pet can swim.

4. it is as yellow as butter.

5. can you tell what my pet is?

Start at 1.
Connect the dots.

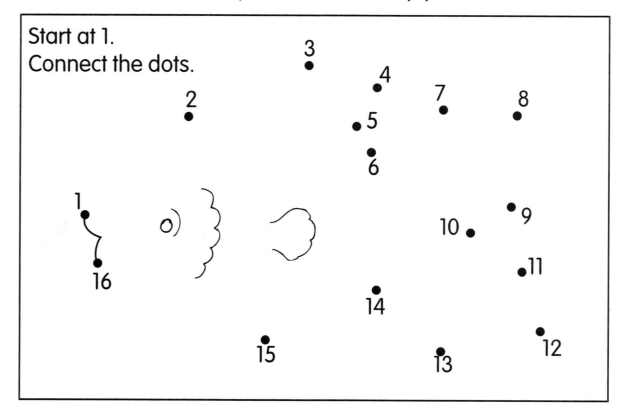

EMC 4023

Write capital letters.
Use periods or question marks.

T
~~t~~he fox is in a box.
C
~~c~~an it get out?

is that a cat

no, it is a skunk

do you like to jump rope

i think it is fun

when did you get that toy

can I play with it

EMC 4023

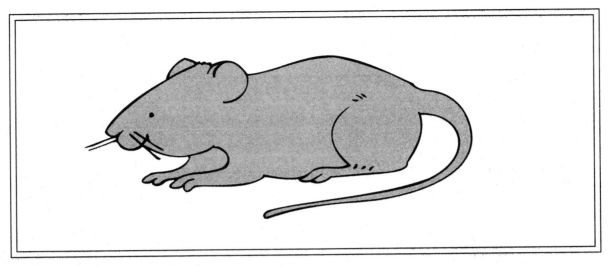

What is missing in this story?

Bud

Can you come over?

my pet rat bud got out

can you help me catch him

i got him

quick, get his pen

lock the lid

thank you

you were a big help

EMC 4023

Who Is It?

he   she   it   we

Write.

_ _ _ _ he _ _ _ _

Match.

it

we

she

he

11

Write.

He   She   We   it

Dad has a box.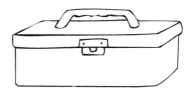

___He___ puts tools in ___it___.

Ted has a red kite.

_____ likes to fly _____.

Ann and I got a big ball.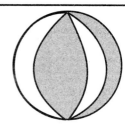

_____ play with _____.

Betty has a bike.

_____ can ride _____.

EMC 4023

One and More Than One

Match.

dog

dogs

cup

cups

can

cans

trees

tree

EMC 4023

One and More Than One

Add <u>s</u> if it is more than one.

cup		

EMC 4023

The Toy Elephant

Color **one** orange.
Color **more than one** brown.

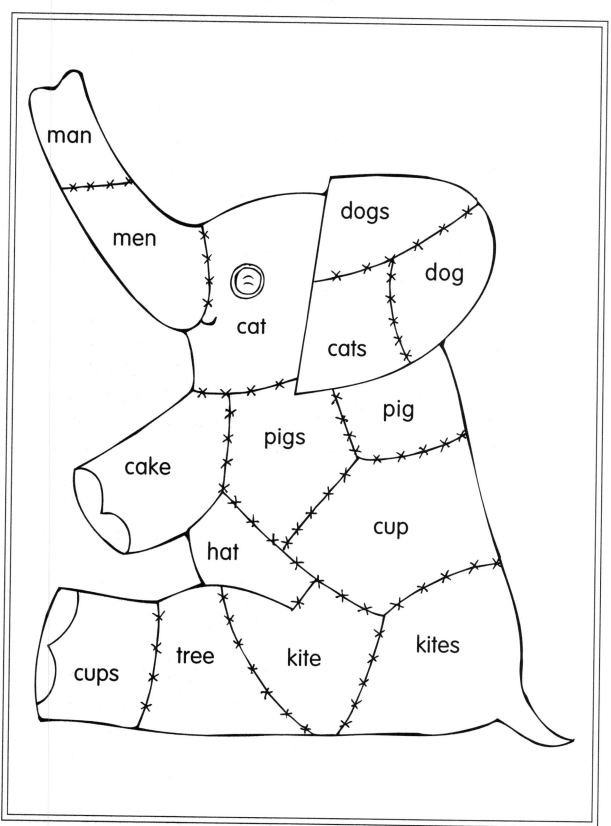

EMC 4023

Making Smaller Words

is not - **isn't**

cannot - **can't**

do not - **don't**

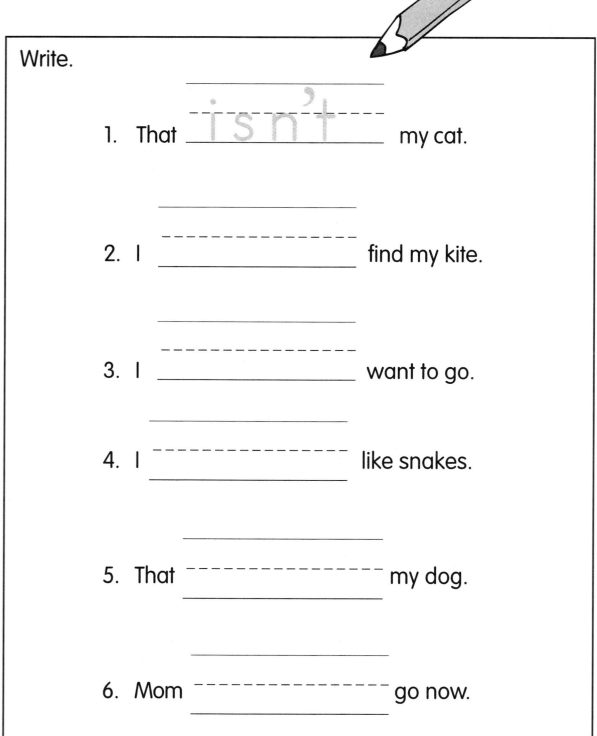

Write.

1. That _____isn't_____ my cat.

2. I _____ find my kite.

3. I _____ want to go.

4. I _____ like snakes.

5. That _____ my dog.

6. Mom _____ go now.

EMC 4023

Match.

isn't   cannot

don't   is not

can't   do not

Write.

1. Bob **cannot** ride a bike.

   Bob __can't__ ride a bike.

2. I **do not** want to go.

   I _____ want to go.

3. That **is not** his pet.

   That _____ his pet.

4. We **cannot** run in the street.

   We _____ run in the street.

EMC 4023

Using <u>is</u> and <u>are</u>

| one - **is** | more than one - **are** |

Circle the right word.

The dog (**is** **are**) small.

Sam and Tom (**is** **are**) here.

My kite (**is** **are**) yellow.

The cats (**is** **are**) playing.

We (**is** **are**) going to Disneyland.

EMC 4023

Using <u>was</u> and <u>were</u>

one - **was**	more than one - **were**

Circle the right word.

His boat ((**was**) **were**) big.

Maria and Jose (**was** **were**) happy.

We (**was** **were**) sleeping.

The sun (**was** **were**) hot.

I (**was** **were**) riding my bike.

EMC 4023

Circle the word.

Bill (**run** (**runs**)) fast.

Ann and Ruth (**run   runs**) too.

The frog (**hop   hops**) to the pond.

Three frogs (**hop   hops**) on the log.

Jose (**ride   rides**) his bike.

His friends (**ride   rides**) bikes too.

EMC 4023

Adding <u>ed</u> and <u>ing</u>

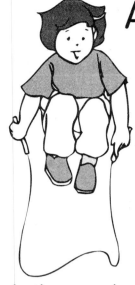

Today I am **jumping** rope.

Yesterday I **jumped** rope.

Circle the word.

The frog is ((jumping) jumped).

The frog (jumping   jumped).

I (hopping   hopped).

I am (hopping   hopped).

The cat is (playing   played).

The cat (playing   played).

Matt is (looking   looked) for his dog.

He has (looking   looked) all day.

EMC 4023

Naming Words

People are **who**.   Things are **what**.

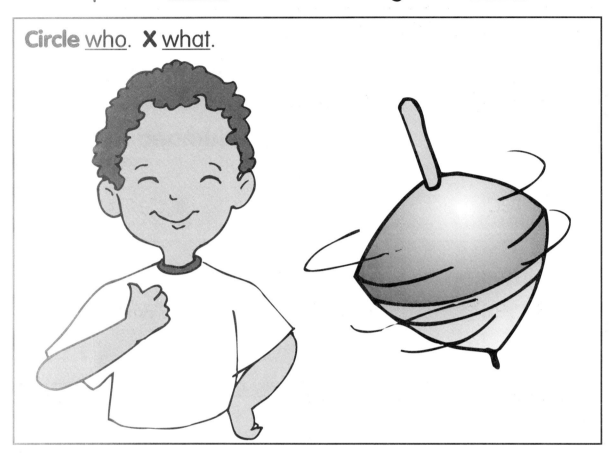

Circle who. **X** what.

Circle who words. **X** what words.

1. (Bill)

2. red top

3. big box

4. clown

5. girl

6. you and me

7. bus

8. yellow kite

9. Mom and Dad

10. trees

EMC 4023

What Am I Doing?

Words that tell what I am doing are called **verbs**.

Put a ring around the <u>doing</u> words.

1. (run)   4. jump   7. sing

2. red   5. table   8. sleep

3. peek   6. hat   9. swim

Draw.

run   sleep

EMC 4023

What Does It Look Like?

Circle the picture that matches the words.

It is big.

It is tall.

It is black.

It is hot.

It is soft.

I see 3.

EMC 4023

Words that Describe

Match the picture and words.
Put a line under the word that tells how it looks.

a fat cat

a small box

a red fox

a hot drink

ten dots

EMC 4023

Find the Surprise

things you can do -   Color **green.**
names of things -   Color **blue.**
how things look -   Color **red.**

box	nut	dog	pig
bed	big	red	ten	six	kite
pan	fast	tall	brown	fat	nest
hop					sit
fox	yell	skip		run	sand
TV		dig		tree	

EMC 4023

Fill in the missing letters.

a b c d e f g h i j k l m n o p q r s t u v w x y z

a ___ c
___ b c
a b ___

___ h i
g ___ i
g h ___

d e ___
d ___ f
___ e f

s ___ u
___ t ___
s ___ v

w x ___
w ___ y
___ x ___ z

___ o p
n ___ ___
n o ___ q ___ r

27

Start at **a**.
Connect the dots.

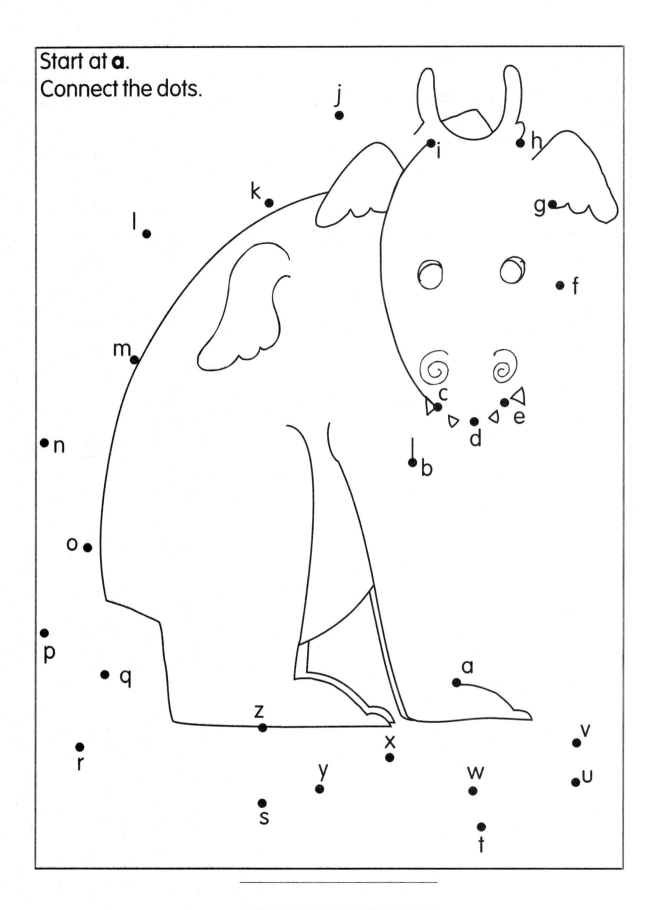

This dragon _____ green.

is   are

EMC 4023

Put the words in ABC order.

a b c d e f g h i j k l m n o p q r s t u v w x y z

1. _____

2. _____

3. _____

bat

chicken

ant

1. _____

2. _____

3. _____

lamb

mouse

kitten

1. _____

2. _____

3. _____

hamster

fox

goat

EMC 4023

Put the words in ABC order.

big   a   cat

_____

- -

_____

gray   five   hats

_____

- -

_____

oranges   my   nine

_____

- -

_____

a b c d e f g h i j k l m n o p q r s t u v w x y z

EMC 4023

Answer Key

Please take time to go over the work your child has completed. Ask your child to explain what he/she has done. Praise both success and effort. If mistakes have been made, explain what the answer should have been and how to find it. Let your child know that mistakes are a part of learning. The time you spend with your child helps let him/her know you feel learning is important.

page 1

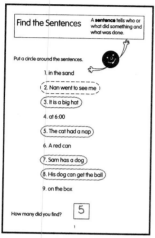

page 2

page 3

page 4

page 5

page 6

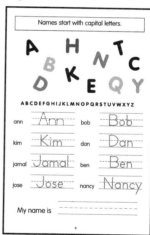

page 7

page 8

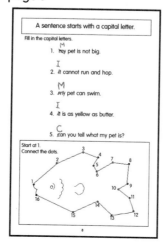

page 9

page 10

What is missing in this story?

Bud

Can you come over?
My pet rat bud got out.
Can you help me catch him?

I got him.
Quick, get his pen.
Lock the lid.

Thank you.
You were a big help.

10

page 11

Who Is It?

he   she   it   we

Trace.

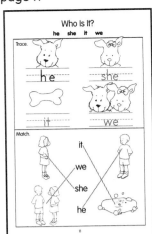

he   she

it   we

Match.

it
we
she
he

11

page 12

Write.   **He   She   We   it**

Dad has a box.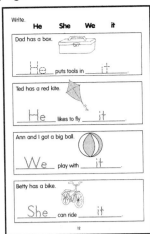

He puts tools in it

Ted has a red kite.

He likes to fly it

Ann and I got a big ball.

We play with it

Betty has a bike.

She can ride it

12

page 13

One and More Than One

Match.

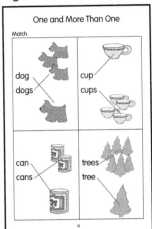

dog
dogs

cup
cups

can
cans

trees
tree

13

page 14

One and More Than One

Add **s** if it is more than one.

cup   pig   hat

ants   hats   cups

pins   pigs   ant

14

page 15

The Toy Elephant

Color **one** orange.
Color **more than one** brown.

15

page 16

Making Smaller Words

is not - **isn't**
cannot - **can't**
do not - **don't**

Write.

1. That isn't my cat.

2. I can't find my kite.

3. I don't want to go.

4. I don't like snakes.

5. That isn't my dog.

6. Mom can't go now.

16

page 17

Match.

isn't   cannot
don't   is not
can't   do not

Write.

1. Bob cannot ride a bike.

   Bob can't ride a bike.

2. I do not want to go.

   I don't want to go.

3. That is not his pet.

   That isn't his pet.

4. We cannot run in the street.

   We can't run in the street.

17

page 18

Using is and are

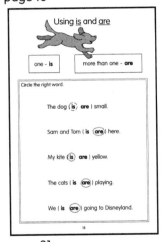

one - **is**   more than one - **are**

Circle the right word.

The dog (**is** are) small.

Sam and Tom (is **are**) here.

My kite (**is** are) yellow.

The cats (is **are**) playing.

We (is **are**) going to Disneyland.

18

page 19

Using was and were

one - **was**   more than one - **were**

Circle the right word.

His boat (**was** were) big.

Maria and Jose (was **were**) happy.

We (was **were**) sleeping.

The sun (**was** were) hot.

I (**was** were) riding my bike.

19

page 20

Circle the word.

Bill (run **runs**) fast.

Ann and Ruth (**run** runs) too.

The frog (**hop** hops) to the pond.

Three frogs (**hop** hops) on the log.

Jose (ride **rides**) his bike.

His friends (**ride** rides) bikes too.

20

page 21

Adding ed and ing

Today I am **jumping** rope.

Yesterday I **jumped** rope.

Circle the word.

The frog is (**jumping** jumped).

The frog (jumping **jumped**).

I (hopping **hopped**).

I am (**hopping** hopped).

The cat is (**playing** played).

The cat (playing **played**).

Matt is (**looking** looked) for his dog.

He has (looking **looked**) all day.

21